Dedicated to Sarah & Simon
and every child who wants
to help the planet

# JUST ONE CHILD

Starting a plastic-free & litter-free journey

Debbie Bartlett

There's a programme on the tele'
And the man is telling me
How plastic is causing problems
For the creatures in the sea.

He says 'Helping wildlife
Is something we all must do'
But how can just one child help?
I'm just a child like you.

I've seen the straws and cans
And the litter on the beach
But what to do about it
Is something they don't teach.

I would like to change the world
But I don't know where to start.
The problems are very **LARGE**
And I'm such a TINY part.

Our bathroom's full of plastic
Shampoos, soaps and body lotion
But now I understand
Plastic is causing problems in the ocean.

There's plastic in my lunchbox
And I don't know what to think.
Mum gives me water in plastic bottles
And puts straws in my drink.

There's plastic rubbish in the town.
It wasn't me who dropped it there.
Why doesn't someone pick it up?
Doesn't anybody care?

So many cigarette ends
Being washed down the drain
Then out into the seas and rivers,
Carried by the rain.

I can't save the whales and dolphins
And the animals in the wild.
What can I do about it?
I'm only **just ONE child**.

*'How can I stop this plastic rubbish?'*
Was my only thought,
As I walked across the beach
And out towards the port.

I'll talk to the ships who have seen
The sharks and fish and whales
And all the plastic in the ocean
I want to hear their tales.

I called out to a **container ship** –
She was as **tall** as she was **LONG**.
She had been to different countries
And could see things going wrong.

She said
'I've seen the animals and birds
Eat our rubbish every day,
Plastic bags and bottles
And other things we've thrown away.'

The mighty **cruise ship** is one
Of the smartest ships at sea.
She laughed when I told her
The problem was nothing to do with me.

The old **tug boat** was very angry
He'd found plastic around the shore.
'It's been bad for many years' he said
'But each day I'm finding more.'

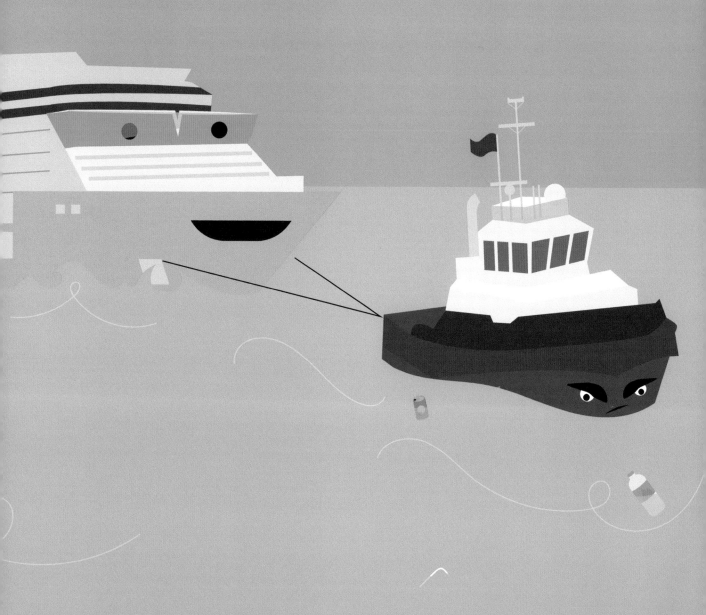

The little wooden **rowing boat**
Had really seen the most.
He had been up the river
And right along the coast.

He said
'Wet wipes, straws and crisp packets
Just never go away.
Your **grandchildren** could be dealing
With what you throw today.'

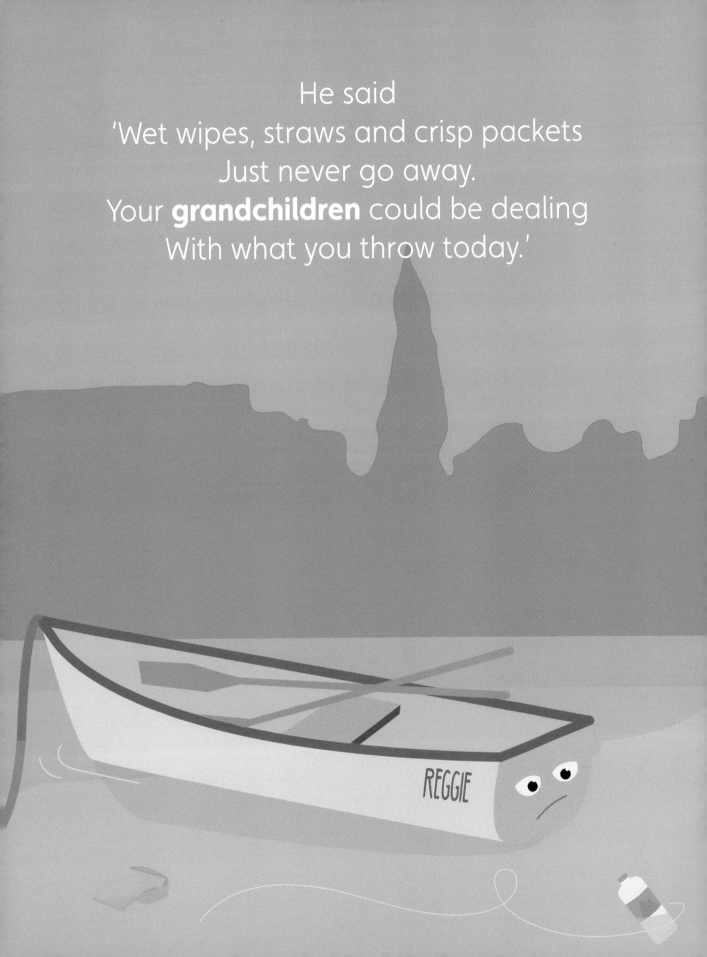

'You think you're just one child
Who cannot rid the sea of plastic
But what if **every** child changed their ways?
Now, wouldn't that be fantastic?'

'So, we're asking you to take some action
And it's really not hard to do.
There's one person who can help the planet
And that person is...

...YOU!

'So please don't use plastic bags and bottles
Or a plastic knife and fork
And **pick up any litter**
When you're out on a walk.'

'When you are in a restaurant,
Remember the animals and think.
Be polite, **refuse the straw** —
You don't need one to drink.'

'And at that birthday party,
**Keep balloons inside** to play.
You don't want wildlife to suffer because
You've let one float away.'

The ships promised to take this message
To children in other lands,
'We will ask **every** child to pick up litter
From river banks and sands.'

'You must re-use, recycle and
Think about what you buy.
Everyone needs to use less plastic,
And **every** child needs to try.'

PICK UP
YOUR RUBBISH

And as I saw the ships sail away,
One winked at me and smiled.
She said 'Together we **can** make a difference.'
It starts with

...JUST
ONE
CHILD

It's our world, our planet,
And this is nothing new
It belongs to all the animals,
Remember it's their world too.

Printed in Great Britain
by Amazon